Juvenilia

Juvenilia

Early Writings of Elizabeth Smart
Edited by Alice Van Wart

The Coach House Press Toronto

Published with the assistance of
the Canada Council and
the Ontario Arts Council.

Archival material reproduced in this book
Courtesy of The National Library of Canada.

Cover photo '"Betty" at eight years'
courtesy of Georgina Barker.

Canadian Cataloguing in Publication Data

Smart, Elizabeth.
    Juvenilia: (early writings of Elizabeth Smart)

ISBN 0-88910-354-2

I. Van Wart, Alice, 1948-   . Title.

PS8537.M37J88 1987   c818'.5409   c87-095251-X
PR9199.3.S564J88 1987

Contents

Part Three, 1929 (15 Years)

Part Four, 1931-1933 (17-19 Years)

Preface

Elizabeth Smart (1913-1986) began writing as a child. At the age of eleven, while she was at the Elmwood School for Girls in Ottawa, she became ill with what was thought to be a leaky heart valve. She spent that year at home and six months in bed. During this time, she read voraciously and began to write daily in a notebook. She also began to learn the names of plants and trees. Both activities sustained her during her illness and recuperation and were to continue for the rest of her life.

Following her illness, Elizabeth returned to Elmwood School for Girls, then went on to Hatfield Hall School for Girls, in Cobourg, Ontario, where she completed her junior matriculation at the age of seventeen. At this point Elizabeth was seriously interested in studying music. Following the summer, spent with her family at their summer home in Kingsmere, she went to England accompanied by her mother, where she was to study piano with the concert pianist Katharine Goodson.

Elizabeth spent the next summer at Kingsmere as well, returning to England in the fall with her sister Jane and a chaperone. During her second year in London, she attended lectures in English Literature and History at the University of London. Her interests gradually moved away from music to literature. However, there were already indications of Smart's literary interests. At the age of sixteen, she had gathered together all her writing from age eleven to that point – stories, poems, satires, a play, and illustrations – into *The Second Edition of The Complete Works of Betty Smart*. From that point, there have been copious notebooks out of which has come her literary work.

The earliest journal that has survived is *The Complete Works of Betty Smart*; it covers the years 1925 to 1933 and contains her juvenilia. The work is varied in form, content, and tone; sometimes it is earnest and sometimes playful. It displays a lively imagination, a strong sense of humour, a romantic sensibility and a satiric eye.

For this book, I have chosen what I think is the best of the juvenilia. I have tampered as little as possible with the prose, correcting spelling errors and punctuation problems only when it seemed necessary, for the sake of clarity. I have also included some early letters Elizabeth wrote to her parents; in the letters I have corrected only the odd spelling error.

Elizabeth Smart's journals are housed in the Literary Archives at the National Library of Canada. The letters were made available to me by Elizabeth Smart before her death.

Once again, I would like to thank Claude Le Moine and Linda Hoad of Literary Archives for their gracious assistance. I would also like to thank Michael Ondaatje for suggesting this project to me and helping to make it possible.

ALICE VAN WART

The Complete Works
of Betty Smart

The Second Edition of The

Complete Works Of
Betty Smart

author of "Wild Foods", "The Perambulating Note book" etc.

---

revised and reviewed by her.

and

Not a Book For Children

Kingsmere

The Betty Publishing Co. Ltd.

1929

To

The Green Monkey
Without whose aid these
Works would never have
been written

Introduction

To begin with these works are not complete, and to continue with they are not works. But other people have made the same mistake, and therefore I am not an original sinner in doing likewise.

In the beginning, hard-hearted reader, you should know that you will not like this book. But for you, that is all the more reason why you should read it.

The satire in 'The Land of Mosquitoes' has never been found out, and perchance never will be. But it is quite plain. 'The Little House,' H.H.R.,* may not seem clear in its meaning, but you have been warned, and take your chance when you read this book.

If you are one of the horrible type, that always reads introductions last, go on your way, for it is too late, and I cannot help you.

Betty Smart
September 21, 1929
Kingsmere
Quebec

* Hard-Hearted-Reader

Part One, 1926

(12 Years)

Heartless Baby

written June 22nd
1926 .12yrs

The woman came weeping into the room; her baby had died just yesterday. Died; really through her fault. Through her tears she looked at its crib, all fresh in crispy white, and, she knew, empty. But as she came nearer she saw it was not! In it was the dearest Budgy Baby, kicking, and cooing and smiling. It was not _her_ baby; she knew it. It was not even _like_ hers. But though she had said she would _never_ look at another baby, this one, somehow, entranced her.

"Oh you darling", she cried, forgetting her sorrow for the moment, "Oh you poor little thing, you have no clothes on."

In a minute it was in her arms, and she was having her most perfect moment. Higher, and higher grew her affection for it. She liked it. She _loved_ it! She _adored_ it!!

"What a cool breeze, I must j shut

Heartless Baby

The woman came weeping into the room; her baby had died just yesterday. Died; really through her fault. Through her tears she looked at its crib, all fresh in crispy white, and, she *knew*, empty. But as she came nearer she saw it was not! In it was the dearest Pudgy Baby, kicking, and cooing and smiling. It was not *her* baby; she knew it. It was not even *like* hers. But though she had said she would *never* look at another baby, this one, somehow, entranced her.

'Oh you darling,' she cried, forgetting her sorrow for the moment. 'Oh you poor little thing, you have no clothes on.'

In a minute it was in her arms, and she was having her most perfect moment. Higher and higher grew her affection for it. She liked it. She *loved* it! She *adored* it!!

'What a cool breeze, I must shut the window,' she said, laying the baby on the bed and going over to the nearest one. 'My darling mustn't catch cold, Oh! no, that wouldn't do at all, would it, Precious?' She looked over the baby – it had gone. Gone out the window – the Pudgy Baby was not there.

Pudgy Baby laughed, as she alighted on a telegraph wire; she laughed fearlessly. Her fat little dimpled legs waved as the breezes blew, and her curly wisps of hair danced over one another. What a lovely time she was having! Four little teeth showed, as she smiled at a big red butterfly.

'Becky! Becky!' called Mrs. Twofoolskin. 'How you *are* neglecting your work. Even if your baby sister *is* sick, and even if you are *not* allowed to see her, it is no reason why there should be no coal in the coal-skuttle, and crumbs on the floor, and dishes unwashed, and silver unpolished, and ...'

And let us say – etcetera.

A red-eyed girl about thirteen bowed her head.

'I'm really sorry mum, I'll do what ye'se tell me right now, and shire I will too.'

She was very tired, and as she was going to the shed for wood, she saw a stump and sat down, lost in her sorrows. Missus was real cross, and when she had gone home for her afternoon off, Mama had been *so* angry, and Baby had been sick, and she had not been allowed to see her. Baby was her one joy, and ...

'Agoo,' said a little voice near her, 'Goo! Goo!'

She looked up and saw beside the shed a once-pink baby, lying on its tummy in the mud, and looking up at her with big, round eyes.

'Oh you Precious Pet! Oh come here! Oh you little sweetheart!' cried Becky in raptures. 'Come to me Darling.'

The baby turned its head away from her, and started creeping towards a tree. She pulled it back, but it slipped out again, and she crept to a bright piece of paper. The paper blew around the corner of the shed; the baby followed. Becky hastened after, but when she got there, the blue-eyed infant was gone!

BLUE-EYED INFANT GONE? – all her sorrows came back.

Blue-eyed infant laughed again as she chased the wind over the meadows. Wasn't it fun to live? Wasn't the world interesting? In her baby mind she thought so.

Men don't cry?? Men *do.* At least Leonard S. McLaine was a man and he was crying. It was divorce that made him cry, not really divorce, but something that had to do with it. *He* didn't mind parting from his wife. She didn't like him at all, though he *did* like her. It was his child. The child was going with his wife. It had always loved him. He had *adored* it. It was their first and only child. It had come after several years of married life. He had *loved* it, and *worked* for it, and *slaved* for it, and now it was going.

A tinkling happy laugh rang out beside him, although he was in a wood, and had chosen the loneliest spot he could find, to think out his faults.

Quickly, and in his mind, he figured that he could live as a hermit, only with this child.

He picked it up in his arms, and sat it on his knees.

'Want to play ride-a-cock-horse?' he asked it, thinking it would lift its arms the way his baby had. It didn't even look at him, but slid off his knees, and picked up a pine-cone. Then it put its baby mouth up to him, and held the pine-cone for him to see. He was entranced! He squeezed it. Still it didn't look at him, and again slid off his knees and started creeping into the woods. Suddenly he awoke to his senses. He went after it. He caught a glimpse of its pudgy toes, sticking out from beside a tree, but when he was there, there was nothing. He sat down. His thoughts deepened, and his troubles grew.

A crow's nest is a very entrancing thing to Pudgy Baby. So much so that she sleeps in one nearly every time she sleeps, either night or day.

Hadn't it been a lovely day? Hadn't she had a lovely time? Pudgy Baby laughed as she curled up in one, and played peek-a-boo with the stars, as one by one they came out. The breezes whispered softly. Pudgy Baby was asleep.

The child was going with his wife.

The Last Dictionary

'I think it is just astounding,' said Mr. Jayde. 'Just think, only fifty-five different kinds of dictionaries, and mostly all the same size.'

'Yes,' agreed Mr. Green. 'I positively have no recollection of anything so absolutely inconsiderate, when we two men (bachelors too) spend our whole life comparing them and learning them by heart.'

'Well,' said Mr. Jayde, 'I suppose, after all, it must be accounted for, that we are about the only well-spoken people, and some people do not apprehend that in the dictionary there are the most absolutely elegantly beautiful words, composed of five syllables.'

Mr. Samuel Jayde, and Mr. Darkney Green were two bachelors, living what would be called a lonely life, but for their dictionaries.

'Well, there's one confoundedly apprehensible thing, and that is that we will not find the fifty-sixth dictionary, that will fill our shelves, and fill our hearts with their desire, if we stay here talking,' said Mr. Green very wisely.

'Righto!' agreed Mr. Jayde, 'I say how rippingly topping you are.'

Mr. Jayde and Mr. Green walked hurriedly along the street on the way to a bookstore.

'I considerably hope,' said Mr. Green, 'that we will find it in this elaborate building.'

'Ah my dear Mr. Green, my uneconomical self greatly desires it,' said Mr. Jayde.

They entered the store and at once said together:

'Have you a dictionary?'

'Ah yes I have,' was the answer.

The hearts of Mr. Jayde and Mr. Green beat very fast. The man came back with five dictionaries.

'Take your choice,' said he.

'Have you no others?' said Mr. Green.

'No sir,' said the man. 'Is this one not to your liking?'

'Well, do you know of any other bookstore in this town?' asked Mr. Jayde.

'Yes,' said the book-keeper. 'Over by Lisping Street beside that big dry-good store.'

Away they hurried, but without any luck. Five more stores they tried, but all in vain. At last they came to a tiny store with everything in it. In they went.

'Have you a dictionary?' they said together.

'Yes,' said the woman, 'I have *one*. Here it is.' And she showed them a little blue one.

'Oh!' gasped Mr. Jayde. 'How wonderfully elegant.'

That night as they poured over the fifty-sixth dictionary, Mr. Jayde said, 'Splendiforous.'

'Fantastic,' said Mr. Green.

'Eqzasperous,' said Mr. Jayde.

We Intellectual Fish

by *Chopin Shumann Dolittle Patrick Fish*

How many of you humans stop to think, when you have to stay in the house, because of the rain, or because of the heat, or because of something else, equally obnoxious, stop to think of us fish, swimming round all day in a glass bowl, with several others of the same species. You complain; we can't, but we wouldn't if we could. All we say is – 'It could be worse.'

Most fish just swim about, and look at the shells, if there are any, or else dart through the castle with a friend. But once in a while there is a fish who has intellect, higher enjoyments, and who is more superior. I am of that kind.

In my bowl there are eight other goldfish, and among them is one who has intellect like I have. He is David. David is a splendid fish, and he is my special friend. I like Glisten, too, and Fantail isn't bad, but David is my *real* chum. I used to have another *real* chum, but a sad misfortune became his.

We had had a very disturbed night, for Smallpox, a little fish that used to be in this bowl, was very sick. Oh so sick! He lay on the top most of the time, but kept trying to swim, which disturbed us fish, who, though we sleep on the bottom of the bowl, see all that happens to the others. But we weren't troubled much longer, for soon he was still. I think he was dead, for he didn't even flap his fins. And when morning came, and a big head looked in, scaring all us fish to the bottom, he didn't move. It was all rather sad, his life flickering out, and no one there to care, but he was a lonely fish, and one of the religious type.

Then, just as Smallpox had been removed, and we were hoping to have a peaceful day, our bowl was lifted up, and we were put in the big basin while our water was being changed. That is not remarkable, for it happens every day; but while we were being lifted out, the top of the plug caught in the net, and the water began to go out very swiftly. That wouldn't have mattered to us, for we were in the net and in a minute would be in our bowl, but there was a fish in the basin that hadn't been caught yet, and he went whizzing down the drain. That fish was my dear comrade Christopher Robin. The hand of the person who was changing our water tried to grab him, but it was too late. Down he went, never to be seen more; but though he is gone, he is not forgotten, by me, David, or our mistress.

That very morning another exciting event took place in our bowl. Two new goldfish arrived. They weren't especially nice. They were too fat, too greedy, and they stared too much. They were called Goggle-eyes and Gogle-eyes, and were fishes of *absolutely NO* intellect at all. Fishes of intellect will take an interest in what goes on outside their bowl as well as in. Of course, even for intellectual fish it is hard to understand. For instance, we see a person walk into the room, and we swim about, and when we look again that person is gone. We can't very well understand what they do, but intellectual fish will *try* to, and *sometimes* succeed. I am one that succeeded, so is David.

The most exciting event that ever took place in our lives, happened just a little while after the death of Smallpox and the sad misfortune of Christopher Robin. Just after our water had been changed, and we were swimming about peaceably, there was a great crash, and we fish found ourselves flopping about in an inch of water. I was the unluckiest of all, for I was thrown farther off under a big dark thing, where there was *practically* no water at all! And worse than that, they didn't find me till a long while after, when I was so weak that I didn't think I would live for more than a day. After that I had salt baths every day, and lay on the top very often, but finally I recovered. David told me afterwards, that the other fish had had a hard time too, for huge black things had been walking about, and they thought that they would be stepped on.

We intellectual fish have noticed lately one person who always stays in one place. (We have learned to recognize her as our mistress.) She lies on her back, but what puzzles us is why she doesn't go up to the ceiling like we do when we're sick. Even intellectual fish are puzzled sometimes.

I forgot to say that before our bowl was broken, four new goldfish arrived, among them Fantail, who, though he had no intellect, is quite a decent fish. Those fish were – Fantail (as I have mentioned), Paperfins, Flapfins, and Giggely-eyes. I was rather jealous of Flapfins, because he had quite a lot of black on him, while before that I was the only one with it. But I didn't have to be troubled long, for in a week he died. David was sorry, for he had always liked Flapfins, but I thought him a rather vulgar fish.

The days pass along quietly. We intellectual fish are *still* trying to make out why our mistress lies still without going to the top of the room. But still, as I said before, even intellectual fish are puzzled sometimes.

26

The First Trip

'Oh my dear companion and comrade,' said Mr. Jayde, 'I feel an – an uncomprehensible desire, to go – now my dear, not for long – to go to London for a fortnight.'

'My word!' was all that Mr. Green said.

'Yes,' continued Mr. Jayde, 'and – Oh my conscience Mr. Green, do not look so forsakenly, I really cannot, Oh I say, I CANNOT continue my profession any longer in this emdominating city!'

'Your *profession*?' gasped Mr. Green. 'Your *profession*?? What is your confounded profession?'

'Oh my word Mr. Green, you *do* give me the hump,' acclaimed Mr. Jayde. 'I heard yesterday, Yes! Uncomprehensible as it is, that there is another kind of dictionary, one that we two old bachelors have not in our possession, and I feel an unresistible desire to own it.'

'Oh yes,' said Mr. Green. 'Ah yes. But why may *I* not go too?'

'My inseparable companion,' said Mr. Jayde, 'I have been invited by Mr. Mosstry to accompany his daughter to London. He didn't want her to go unaccompanied, and he has known me since his boyhood.'

'Ah, I comprehend,' said Mr. Green. 'I comprehend now.'

'Oh Mr. Green! Mr. Green!' called Mr. Jayde the next day. 'I say, which necktie shall I wear?'

'Pardon?' said Mr. Green, hurrying into the room, 'I didn't quite get that.'

'I asked you which necktie you thought I should wear,' answered Mr. Jayde.

'Oh. That bright red one with the black and yellow spots will do very well for the occasion,' said Mr. Green.

'My word Mr. Green,' said Mr. Jayde, 'not with this tweed suit; I pronounce it too brilliantly coloured.'

'Well,' said Mr. Green, 'that blue one striped with yellow is of my approval.'

'Mr. Green! Mr. Green!' said Mr. Jayde. 'Recollect that elaborate looking man we saw about a month ago, wearing a blue tie striped with yellow with a tweed suit, and remember how uncomfortably consciously embarrassed he was when *everybody*, mind now, Mr. Green, *everybody*, stared at him.'

'Yes,' said Mr. Green slowly, 'I do. Well then, how about *this* extravagant one?'

'No,' said Mr. Jayde very decidedly.

'Well,' said Mr. Green, 'which one do *you* want?'

'Humph!' said Mr. Jayde. 'I don't seem to know. Ah yes! I think, after all, that bright red one spotted with yellow will do excellently.'

Mr. Jayde was all ready to go, and was in the train, when he remembered that he had forgotten his valise.

'Oh I say! Mr. Green,' he cried excitedly. 'Run home and get my valise.'

'My word!' said Mr. Green. 'The train leaves in two minutes.'

'Don't stop,' yelled Mr. Jayde. 'Hurry! Hurry!'

Mr. Green was just appearing with the valise when the train jerked.

'Throw it! Throw it!' cried Mr. Jayde almost in tears. 'Quickly!'

Mr. Green did so but it was too late. The valise fell onto the tracks, and the train puffed out of sight with Mr. Jayde wailing and lamenting loudly.

'Well! Well! Well! My word! I say,' said Mr. Green. 'What *will* Mr. Jayde do?'

'Is this yours, Sir?' said a porter, hurrying up to Mr. Green with the greasy valise.

'Well, er – er – well – in reality, in *reality* it is,' said Mr. Green.

He then looked at the clock.

'Yes, yes,' said he, 'only 9:30 A.M. I have plenty of time to stay and watch the trains. Yes,' and with another glance at the clock, '*plenty* of time.'

He sat down on a bench with his pipe, intending to learn a bit about trains by observation. But pretty soon he was nodding. You see he had had *such* a disturbed night. Mr. Jayde had been so excited that he could not sleep, and turned and talked, and, to tell the truth, Mr. Green hadn't been much better, for it was Mr. Jayde's first trip.

The porters were all in a very excited condition.

'Shall I, or shall I not wake him?' asked one.

'I don't know,' said another. 'But I heard him say 9:30 A.M., and then something else, so I suppose he wanted to catch that train.'

'Well,' said another, 'last time when I didn't wake someone who had fallen asleep, and so lost his train, I got an awful scolding from the boss, nearly lost my job.'

'What y'talking about?' asked a newsboy.

'That gent over there with the greasy valise beside him,' said they.

'Want me to wake him?' said he.

'That's what we want to know,' they answered. But at last it was decided that they should *not* wake him.

The hours past along. Mr. Green still slept. He woke up once and went to a restaurant and got his lunch, but came back again and was soon nodding. It was just dusk and there was nobody at the station, for the trains had either left or come. Mr. Green was just waking up when he saw a little man hurrying down the tracks.

'I say! Is that you Mr. Green?' asked the little man.

'Yes! Yes!' said Mr. Green. 'And who are you?'

'Don't you recognize me? Oh you do aggrieve me,' said Mr. Jayde, for it was he.

'Yes, of course. But my word!' said Mr. Green. 'How did you get here?'

'Well!' puffed Mr. Jayde. 'When I found I hadn't my valise, I got off the train the first time it stopped, and, though it was not at all to my liking ran home. Now of course I stopped to eat at an inn, but I only stopped once, and Oh I say, I *am* hungry.'

'Yes. Yes,' mumbled Mr. Green. 'My word! Oh! Oh!'

'Well, and where is my unwellbehaved valise?' asked Mr. Jayde.

'Oh right there Mr. Jayde,' said Mr. Green. 'Do not be so unattractively demanditive.'

'Oh I say,' wailed Mr. Jayde. 'My valise *does* look disrespectful, what *shall* I do?'

'You will have to wait till tomorrow, I rightly prophesize,' said Mr. Green.

'What will poor Miss Mosstry do?' said Mr. Jayde. 'And what will Mr. Mosstry *say*?'

'That will be as it may,' said Mr. Green. 'Now we will start for our usual abode.'

'Yes! Yes!' said Mr. Jayde. 'Righto! Yes! Yes!'

The next day Mr. Jayde was off, valise and all *this* time. Mr. Green looked mournful.

'Why couldn't I have gone?' he murmured. 'I am economical, unselfconscious, dictionarish, and languishable, and I also have a liking for attractively pretty girls.'

He sat down on a bench, murmuring what he had learnt about trains, when people began to flock in, and he was startled by a whistle.

'Oh I simply *cannot* miss the delicious sight of a moving train,' said he. 'And I especially admire and like to see all the people.'

Many people got off; but there was one whom he seemed to recognize. He screwed up courage.

'Am – am – am – I addressing Miss Mosstry?' said he.

'You are,' said she.

'It would be a very great honour if you would give me the pleasure of allowing yourself to be accompanied home by me,' said Mr. Green.

'Thank you very much,' said she.

As soon as he had taken her home he exclaimed, 'My word, this is a mix-up.'

Next day at noon, whom should arrive but Mr. Jayde.

'I went to London anyway,' said he. 'And there are many elaborate and beautiful buildings, and – Oh! Mr. Green, I got the dictionary, and where is Miss Mosstry?'

'Her dear father is escorting her home,' said Mr. Green. 'He left this morning.'

'Oh Mr. Green!' said Mr. Jayde, 'and I wanted to propose to her.'

'Never mind Mr. Jayde,' said Mr. Green. 'You would have *had* to have new shoe-laces for the wedding and you spent all your money on the dictionary.'

'Yes,' said Mr. Jayde. 'You're right. And anyway, I do not want to be a hardworking husband man. I want to be a comfortable old bachelor.'

Woodland Tragedy

It was spring. All the world was awakening. All the birds were returning. Among the returning birds were two robins, full of enthusiasm.

All around they flew, searching high and low for a suitable place to put their precious nest that they were to build. No. No. *That* tree would not do; it was too low, yes, and too small. Why! the babies might fall out with such small forking. No – not that either, that would be too sunny. But at last a place was chosen; it was right under the eaves of a veranda; nobody used it; there were plenty of worms in a flower bed nearby, and it was sheltered from the wind and rain.

Then began the building. Oh how hard they worked, hardly stopping to eat or sleep. Yes! Yes! Hurry! It must be finished soon. Hurry! Hurry! No, no, *that* bit of mud had a stone in it, it would spoil the nest. What labour! But at last it was finished. How they looked with pride at it. Finished and complete!

A little later a butterfly flitting past, saw in the nest four beautiful blue eggs. Oh how great was the robins' pride. The nest was *nothing* compared with this. Oh the long and dreary hours the mother bird spent on that nest. But what would be the reward? Ah! That would be worth a *year* of sitting. Just a few more days, just a few. Oh how great their joy would be, oh how great!

Oh keep away! Keep away! Don't come a step nearer. Stay back. Don't you know that the robins have a nest and four eggs on this veranda? Go away – come not near – but alas it was hopeless. Six human beasts tore down the nest, and blew the eggs out of the shells. Oh how great was the robins' sorrow! Oh how they grieved! There is still one left! Oh put it back in the nest. Oh leave it unharmed. Now that one is gone too. Oh how *can* you? It is mean, cruel, and cowardly. The robins think not of that. They only grieve.

Another nest was nearly built. Though they showed no sorrow, deep down in the heart of each was a sad, sad spot. But hope was springing. The nest was not on a veranda, it was in a pine. The days were cool and warm, and the world was happy.

There were four eggs. Yes. Four of the bluest most beautiful eggs that there ever were, and day and night they were guarded with utmost care.

Half coiling, half gliding, up the tree came an ugly, ugly snake. Robins! Hurry to your nest, your eggs are in danger! Just for one tiny minute had they left it.

One egg is gone; three remain. Down goes a second. But who are these two furious persons, flying so swiftly in this direction? Then the snake thought it time to retire. Down the tree he went, and away, away to do more mischief.

Only two! Only two! But they would soon be hatched. In a few days there was a hungry, featherless little bird in the nest. Their first child. What a work it was to keep it fed! But what a joy!

There was still one egg in the nest. One still unhatched. It too would soon be a baby; another hungry little robin to be kept fed.

But down below the tree, every day, walked human beasts. How the birds' hearts beat at the time! Then one day the father bird came no more. The mother had seen it. Seen the hawk glide silently down. She screeched; but it was too late. She was alone. Alone, and beside herself with grief. Still there was hope for the unhatched egg, and still the baby had to be fed.

Could it be? No it could not! But it was. It was true. Up the tree was climbing a hideous, a hideous human beast. Up to her nest it came. Its hand went into it. 'Don't touch my babies! Leave them there!' ... The human screeched. Down the tree it went again, and Oh! what joy! The egg and the babe were unharmed!

Then came the flying lessons for the hatched baby. It was hard to learn to fly. But yes, it found that if it held its wings out, it could go higher, or along, or any way it liked. It was becoming quite accustomed to flying, and was out on a lesson, when up the tree again climbed the beastly human. Up to her nest, and what? Oh it was sad, for the human was handling her egg. Yes – her precious egg! Then it cracked and split. Yes! The egg was broken.

Down the tree went the human. Down it went. Oh it was sad, and it was the *only* egg. The mother robin wept. Wept for her egg.

The False Curl

Mrs. Tampyhead was a female, and a female she was. For she was not a woman, and *not* a lady, and *certainly not* a Queen! She had, unfortunately, one seventeen year old daughter, and more unfortunately still, a husband who *was* a man. But prized above all her jewels, husband, daughter, clothes, or anything, was her one false curl which she wore pinned into her hair by a big safety-pin, right in the middle of her forehead. It was her only bit of curly hair, and she prized it greatly. Her daughter *hated* it. Yes she did. So one time she got a horse to eat it in the night. Yes she did. And when the female, Mrs. Tampyhead woke up – What! It was gone.

'You *will* give it back. You *will*.' She muttered to herself, and went back into the room where her daughter slept. 'Gimme my curl,' she said.

But her daughter only smiled sweetly in her sleep.

In the Land of the Mosquitoes: A Satire

'What was that? My stars!' exclaimed Adelaide Mosque, a member of a *very* large tribe of people called the tribe of the Common Mosquitoes.

Slap! Slap! Slap!

'Anthony Mosque, *do* come here, I heard a slapping, slapping, slapping, I can't imagine – unless ...'

'Unless, my own dear Adelaide Mosque, it was a meal man.'

'My heart beats, and yet my stomach craves,' remarked Adelaide.

'The stronger always wins, and that means your stomach,' said Anthony.

Adelaide Mosque was already away, dining on hot blood (which to her is like corn-on-the-cob to you or me).

Anthony soon joined her, and followed her wise example.

'I'm not a grumbler, or a fault finder, but I got this man first, and I have a right to it. The man was made for you and me,' she added confidently, as she had had a *very* thorough education, a rare and expensive one. 'I'm generous though, and will allow you and your friend Jonathan Mosquit, and his wife Annabelle Beatrice, and our few hundred children who have stayed in this region.'

All the Mosque children received a very good education, especially in Natural History, Physical Geography, and ordinary History.

School was held on a man's shirt collar, if possible, or else by the brooklet, on a mossy log.

All lined up in rows, each at attention, all eagerness for the very first lesson. Loved by all, big and little, human, animal, insect, and vegetable, a lesson all must learn. That lesson was eating. Next to that was Natural History.

'First of course,' said the teacher, 'in all the order of creatures comes the Common Mosquitoe.' (As each animal (man included) puts *himself* first on the long list, so did the mosquitoes.)

'Why!' said a young one at his first lesson. 'We're most important. Most important in the whole wide world.'

'Even so!' replied the philosophic Mosque child.

'Next on our list comes the house fly, who is almost equalled by the black fly,' continued the teacher. 'Not much is known of the others, except of course, the man. But the *man* was only made to eat, and it would be mere foolishness to put it on the list.'

Then school was over for the young ones, and they went flying home to have their feet licked by their mother, because of the nice manny taste left on them.

Adelaide, their mother, always counted on this dainty which her generous children gave her at once, because they could not reach it themselves.

'I wonder what it tastes like?' remarked the young one. 'Maybe like our manny meat does.'

'Even so!' replied the philosophic Mosque child.

'Goodbye my cutie,' said Adelaide Mosque as she hurried to the tubby toe of a baby. 'If you're hungry visit the store of manny meat – Goodbye – I may never see you again.'

'My Anthony! My Anthony! I am suffering in agony,' cried Adelaide as she returned from her meal of hot blood of baby blood. 'That man-meat has broken one of my legs. Oh!' and she fainted away.

Aren't you *sorry* for Adelaide Mosque?

'Oh Samuel Mosquit, do come and see the dear hundred new brothers and sisters I've just got. More'll be hatched in a jiffy or so – but aren't these darling?' said a young Mosque child.

'Rather,' replied the other mosquitoes. 'We had seventy-five about a sun-moving inch ago. But I hear the school buzzing!'

'Late as usual,' remarked the teacher of the Mosque children. 'Today we will take up Scripture. Of course, as you know, Jacob Mosquitoesy was the first living thing on earth.'

'Oh just think!' said a young one on his second lesson. 'To be the only thing alive. How lovely! Wouldn't it be fun?'

'Even so!' replied the philosophic Mosque child.

Part Two, 1928

(14 Years)

The Birth of a Genius

The evening sets, the sun goes down, and still the child sits on the stump of the Mushroom Forest. He cannot leave; he cannot move; he is being told a secret. (And such a secret we, even we, will not be told. It is the secret that the trees have known for ages. *They* never tell it, only in the winter; but can they not be forgiven for that: Because all summer long the birds beg to be told. What is it that the trees keep whispering, whispering all day long? – ah no, you must not ask, they are answered; and so the birds fly south, and the trees have their secret – but they are alone. Oh trees! Now are you sorry? – The trees bow down their heads for shame, and a whistling wail is borne upon the wind. *Now* they are *alone* – No! For a chickadee is calling in his softest voice – they will remain if they are told, and lo! the trees have whispered their secret, and still the chickadee keeps calling in his softest voice.) The voices of the trees are telling the child, and he cannot move. He is filled, and yet he does not know. A spirit is about him, and the Mushroom Forest is full of music. The child is lifted up, and borne to the top of a pine tree. What he sees we shall not be told, but it is something wonderful, beautiful, and – well, after you have said that, what is left? Then just as slowly, just as gently, he is borne down to earth again. While the Mushroom Forest is filled with music.

When a genius is born he is just as any other baby. But his real birth is when he is lifted up through the musical air of Mushroom Forest.

The Little House

The child left the house with a feeling of great joy in her. The last time she had left it a tear had been trying to sneak out, and there was no reason. The mistress of the little house was sick, and the child had covered her with a blanket and kissed her forehead. The child was a child, and the mistress of the little house was not a child, but she had kissed her forehead, and left her sleeping.

The sun was large, and was melting into the sky, and the pine trees were silhouetted against it. The child was well on her way now, but she looked back, and saw the dear little house standing bravely out, as if *it* were not afraid of the dark. She thought of the mistress of the little house, the kiss, and a chokey feeling came up inside her.

'She's only a child, after all,' thought the child.

It grew dark, and still, and the child went home....

The end of this.

(Do you not see the point? Ah! I thought as much.)

Mrs. MacPhail's Earrings

Ella was at church, and Ella was feeling religious. She was singing all the hymns, and closing her eyes, and really being *awfully* good. The sermon was being given and Ella was watching the minister and listening. But her eyes (all by themselves, of course) sort of began going down (you know how they do) until suddenly – she saw the earrings! (I could not describe them except as blobs of pearls on chains.) Then, suddenly, Ella's religious spirit flew away, her piousness went too; everything went, except, alas, those earrings.

They belonged to Mrs. MacPhail. (Poor dear simple lady, forgive Ella's little pot (it is getting bigger) of hate; after all, dear lady, *you* do not see them all the time.) Ella's little pot was a boiler; in fact, she would have given anything to pull them off, *violently*! A raging tempest was raging in Ella in the peaceful church. But she got up and went out, because everybody else was doing that....

'Ella, child, what has happened?!!'

'Nothing?' Oh yes, more than you could think of. 'Ella, child, why this victorious look of triumph?' Did she sleep well? Ella doesn't know what happened, nor does she care, because she spent the night pulling off Mrs. MacPhail's earrings!

But how did you get them off? I do not know. But I do know they are off. Ella wanted Mrs. MacPhail's head treated in the same manner, but you have to draw the line somewhere. So I let the poor, dear, simple lady live.

Mister Winks

When you see Mister Winks you always say to your friend, or yourself: 'There goes Mister Winks.' And you laugh to yourself 'Russian 5% Stock,' and your friend says, 'What?' and you say it again, but loudly this time, and she (or he) always makes wrinkles in her brow and says 'Uh?' But you never explain because you can't. All those questions have taken so much time that all we can see of Mister Winks now is the end of his coat-tail moving gaily in the breeze as he hurries (where Oh where?? But nobody knows) out of sight. So we shall have to let him hurry into the future, while we walk slowly back into the past. (We shall not go right back to the time when Mister Winks was biting his pencil and working addition sums, because we could never remember a time when he didn't have coat-tails.)

Mister Winks is talking with a business man who knows about stocks and shares.

'Russian 5% Stock,' the man is saying, and now it is Mister Winks' turn to say 'What?' Mister Winks is not very good at remembering things, but he thinks perhaps he can manage this.

'Russian 5% Stock,' says Mister Winks hurrying off. And that is how it all began.

It is really a tragedy, and you must not laugh. Mister Winks is sixty-three, and it has been going on for fourteen years. He will get over it, and yet I often wonder: How is it all the youthful maidens dodge the corners and make eyes? Yes it is one of the tragedies of life. Everyone avoids him. Perhaps he knows this, and so hurries away to find the old self he used to be. I do not know, and yet I often wonder.

Here he comes. Shall we dodge? or wait to hear the same old story? We shall wait.

'Russian 5% Stock,' mutters Mister Winks, and his coat-tails hurry away after him.

March 8, 1928

The Baby Nymph

Where the water-lilies floated upon the pond and the ducklings swam about among the cat-tails lived the Baby Nymph. She had a water-lily in her hair, and the ducklings were her playmates. She had one of her toes in the water, and she watched the bright blue-bottle darting out above it; it was not the only one, no, there were many blue-bottles; and down at the bottom of the pond was a gold fish.

Far away there was a house, and in it a man was wringing his hands. This was a rarity, for he was a strong man, and up in the ways of the world. He caught sight of a water-lily, but a water-lily is a happy thing, and the eyes of the man were dull with tears. How should *he* know what that symbolism meant? He would have felt the sun, but his body was too cold to feel, and his mind was too full of his sorrows to think about the little ducks, had he caught a glimpse of them. No, we cannot help this man, and we must leave him to his fate.

The pond is filling cried the frog. But nobody heard him. If he does not stop his crying the man will flood the pond. What is a man that he should cry? If he does not stop it will be *he* who has drowned the Baby Nymph. In his sorrow he does not know.

The woods lay cool and still, and the pond and the Baby Nymph were lapped up, and they were seen no more. The man is crying still, and he will never know what happened. He will never forget his sorrows, but the woods will always eye him suspiciously. They do not know his story, and he does not know their secret. He is ashamed of his crying now. But have they no better reason to be ashamed of him? Yes, and sometimes they sigh and moan for the Baby Nymph, but she will not come back. She is gone and they will have to weep.

will always eye him suspitiously. They
do not know his story, and he does
not know their secret. He is
ashamed of his crying now. But have
they not better reason to be ashamed
of him? Yes, and sometimes they sigh
and moan for the baby nymph, but she
will not come back. She is gone, and
they will have to weep.

The END

Part Three, 1929

(15 Years)

November, 1929

Patty Duh Fwaw Grass Sandwidges:

A One-Act-One-Scene Play

Instructions and Warning For Those Who Wish To Read Them:
In the first place, this play has no Point, Plot, or Pretty Part; it is
merely a Thing.

The Scene is a church basement (a very genteel one), where
six odd ladies are enjoying afternoon tea. The majority of these
ladies are middle-aged, and two possess, respectively, one Pek-
inese and one poodle of nondescript breed.

Mrs. Grunty who is of great interest, as she provides the
name for the play, is plain, fat, decidedly slovenly, and middle-
aged. She wears button boots, which are worn down at the heel,
and her hair has grown wispy from eating too much. It often
happens that the ends fall over her face, and her tall, shiny,
shapeless hat, which perches on top of her head, displays them to
the best of advantage.

Mrs. Purety is a watery-eyed female, with the poodle of the
nondescript breed, whom she calls Lovey. She is quite thin, and
her clothes are too large for her. She is a real missionary worker,
and the only one, in fact, who came this afternoon apart from the
idea of the tea.

Mrs. de Frills is dressed with genteel taste and good-breeding,
but despite this she has a flavour of churchiness about her.

Miss Linton is only thirty-five, and the youth and life of the party. She considers herself the last word in tact. She is dressed in mauve, and hopes she looks thirty-four.

The other characters *Mrs. Weesh* and *Mrs. Maloney* are fat, and wear respectively silk and serge.

Mrs. Maloney, the serge lady, is rather blunt in manner, but kind, very kind.

Mrs. Weesh sways to emotion, and writes poetry at home sometimes. She is rather a sentimental lady.

Lovey, Mrs. Purety's poodle of nondescript breed wears an elegant bow of pink satin around his manly neck. He is the only gentleman at the party, and behaves accordingly. He is, however, resentful of the pink bow.

These are the characters.

Now for the play.

Ist Act – 1st Scene

MRS. GRUNTY: Please pass the patty duh fwaw grass sandwidges. (The other ladies cast angry glances at Mrs. G. because she has shown great absence of self-control in asking for the sandwiches made by Mrs. de Frills, the High Hat lady, for this memorable charity tea. Besides, patty de foi grass sandwiches mark a distinct social attainment, and there are only five left anyway, not counting the decorate. However, these ladies consider that manners maketh the higher sex of man, so glaringly give in.)

MRS. WEESH: Those cunning little button bags that Ellen's sister-in-law made, didn't sell as quick as I thought they would.

MRS. MALONEY: Well, I guess this being a holiday most of the folks would be at the show – still, I saw Mamie Legett's mother-in-law's niece there with her two girls, nice big girls they are too

– and she not being a regular church attendant I was real surprised.

MRS. PURETY: I think –

MISS LINTON: I was saying –

MRS. PURETY: Do go on.

MISS L: Finish what you were syaing Mrs. Purety.

MRS. GRUNTY: (seizing her opportunity) Please pass the patty duh fwaw grass sandwidges. (However this remark is unobserved – the tactful Miss Linton being preoccupied.)

MRS. PURETY: I was only going to say that I think, as this is the last meeting of the Woman's Mission and Helpful Society for this year, that there ought to be a speech made by someone. (There is general startlement and confusion.)

MRS. M: (seeking favour) Mrs. de Frills, wouldn't you?

MRS. DE F: I am so sorry, but I simply must refuse. I have a most frightful cold and the doctor wishes me to rest my voice for a day or two. (If it were any but this High Hat lady the others would ask one another sourly why, under those conditions, she came to a conversational tea at all, but seeing it is *the* Mrs. de Frills it is different.)

MISS LINTON: Oh we are so sorry, dear Mrs. de Frills, but we understand perfectly. Wouldn't Mrs. Maloney be so kind? I have heard of her capability for speech-making.

MRS. M: That's real kind of you Miss Linton, but if you don't mind I don't feel so good myself.

MISS L: Of course not.

MRS. WEESH: (dying to be asked) Mrs. Grunty? (The latter not hearing the conversation, but seeing at last someone taking notice of her, seizes her opportrunity.)

MRS. G: Please pass the patty duh fwaw grass sandwidges.

(This is too much for the irate ladies of the Mission Society, and they resent it.)

MRS. P: (ignoring the vulgar remark pertaining to the food) Would you make us a little speech, Mrs. Grunty? We all think it would be very appropriate as a little Farewell to our little weekly meetings.

MRS. G: (rather confused) Well, now! But why don't you? (She is rather a crude creature, but it must be remembered that she didn't have the advantages of this Helpful Mission in her youth.)

MRS. P: (pinking) I hope you didn't think I was suggesting myself? I entirely forgot that I might be – er – called upon. But, of course, if you really wish it –

MISS L: (the tactful) Oh surely, I think it would be very appropriate, as you have suggested it. (All mumble ungracious agreement, except Mrs. W. who is genuinely glad.)

MRS. P: Well, er, thank you ladies and dear friends. I feel this an honour too deep for mere words. Er – Er – As we are all gathered together for the last time this season – I – I – er – er – I hope you ladies will excuse me if I just glance at some notes I had made beforehand, just in case – I were – er – called upon – I hope you don't think I thought – er –

MISS L: (ever to the rescue) Oh no, certainly not Mrs. Purety – do let us have it.

MRS. P: Ladies and – er – ladies, er Dear ladies. I think, one and all of us ought to be very thankful that we have, one and each, been able to do our small bit in helping to make this world a better place for the little Lambs of God in the lower regions of Africa, and establishing friendship between the higher and lower races of Mankind (waxing eloquent). It is only by being unselfish and giving things away to the poor that we are able to show our superiority. For instance, those sweet little bootees that our Mrs. Maloney made show that she is higher than the subjects of our Mission meetings. (She thinks this is rather neat, but our Mrs. M. winces, and Mrs. de F. shows her good breeding by being decidedly horrified.) And I think we all ought to sing a hymn of praise to show our deepfelt thanks for having been shown the Great Truth. (Mrs. W. is clearly moved, and is almost in tears.) Could Miss Linton do us the honour of leading us?

MISS L: (off her guard) – er – I – what hymn shall we sing, Mrs. Purety?

MRS. P: What would you think, Miss Linton?

MISS L: Whatever you wish, Mrs. Purety.

MRS. P: Well, as a matter of fact, I brought the music to 'Onward Christian Soldiers' just in case it was thought appropriate to sing one.

MRS. M: We all know the words.

MRS. P: Miss Linton, you share with me, and then you can lead the singing. (The song proceeds; Mrs. P.'s clear sweet voice radiating over all. She is, of course, in the lead; and when it is finished, her eyes are all dewy, etc., and Mrs. W. is sniffling.)

MRS. P: I thought – (what next?)

MRS. M: What did you think?

MRS. P: A little prayer for the Missionaries –

MRS. M: Sure dear, if you know one.

MRS. P: O yes, I composed one this morning. Of course, I am not for a minute suggesting that we should have it, but if we were stuck – I have a copy of it with me. I brought it along with me, just in case I was – er – called upon, you know, my dears – I *hope* you won't think me protrooding, but I always like to be on the safe side.

MRS. DE F: (grandly) Certainly, Mrs. Purety, do let us have it.

MRS. P: Er – hsa – could we kneel? It adds glamour to the artistic side of the prayer – you know.

MISS L: (embarrassed) Oh, of course.

OTHERS: (awkwardly) Certainly. (Or if of Mrs. M.'s type) Sure.

MRS. P: It's in verse (startlement). (Reading passionately):

Let us think of the missionaries
Being noble and true,
Helping poor lost lambs
All their life through.

Refrain:
Oh help Mission's Work
So they mayn't their duty shirk.

Let us be like them
Let each one strive
To lead an uplifted
And beautiful life.

Refrain:
Oh help Mission's Work
So they mayn't their duty shirk.

Oh see the sunlight!
Shining on the Earth
Let us resemble it,
Without shameful mirth.

Refrain:
Oh help Mission's Work,
So they mayn't their duty shirk.

Amen

(This poetic prayer does not rank among the highest in the annals of English Literature, but it shows the lofty ideals of Mrs. P.'s mind.)

MRS. W: (the only one truly moved) Mrs. P. that's grand! Just grand, Mrs. P!

MRS. P: (modestly) Oh, just a little thought of mine; it came to me like the flutter of the wings of a tiny bird.

MRS. W: Say! (She is speechless with admiration.)

(Mrs. P. wanting to make an artistic exit, now says her adieus and departs with poodle, wrapped in ecstasies and deep aspirations.)

(Mrs. M. is struggling with her galoshes, and Mrs. W. would like to offer her aid, but does not like to descend from the high plane of thought with which she is mingling.)

MRS. M: (hinting) These galoshes are last year's make and don't fit as good as this year's. They're all a bit too heavy, Amie says, and she says they ought to be cut down and ...

MRS. W: (descended from the skies in any event) Couldn't I be of any help?

MRS. M: If you would be that kind, dearie. I was saying to Amie only last Toosday that it's little things that make you fond of folks. (After she has been assisted into her coat, hat, gloves and scarf, and likewise Mrs. W., Mrs. M. finds her bag missing.)

MRS. M: (looking under a cushion) It's not what you call a

pretty bag, Mrs. Weesh, but it's practical. I was saying to Amie only yesterday, it's not looks but usefulness that counts in life. (One of her higher moments.)

MRS. W: Yes, that's right. Would it be a large-sized one?

MRS. M: Well, I would say yes. You see, I always like something genteel to carry home the chickens from market – something not so vulgar, you know. And as I was saying, it's not looks but usefulness that counts.

MISS L: (ever to the rescue) Is this it, Mrs. Maloney?

MRS. M: The same!! Thank you Miss Linton, I'm real grateful to you; and this has been a very delightful tea, I assure you. Well, goodbye all.

ALL: Goodbye, Mrs. Maloney.

MRS. W: Do wait a moment Mrs. M. and I'll walk home with you as far as Toss Street. I'd like to see those embroidered cloths you're crocheting. Goodbye. (Exit after Mrs. M. in a flurry.)

(Mrs. G., the bugaboo of an otherwise genteel party is struggling with her rubbers and her conscience. There is still one sandwich of her choice left – could she risk the high hat eyes of Mrs. de F.? It is a debatable question, but Mrs. G. was always a gracious soul, and now, nothing loath, gives in.)

MRS. DE F: (sarcastically) Would you like another cup of tea, Mrs. Grunty?

MRS. G: (where is the woman's pride?) No thanks, Mrs. de Frills. Poor dear Henry used to say that it's all right to eat, as long as you don't wash it down with beverages. Those was his very words. 'You know,' he says, 'you'll be troubled with your old indigestion again if you don't be careful,' he says to me, he says. And I believe him, because I'd rather play safe than take the punishment. (This is her only vocal tribute to the party, and it is rather a useful piece of information besides. Quite an accomplishment for Mrs. G. However, the other ladies, with their genteel upbringings, can never forgive her for humiliating them about the *pâté de foie gras* sandwiches, and she will ever be an Awful Example to them.)

MRS. G: (ready to go at last) Well, I told Lucy I'd be home at 5:30, and I don't like to keep the poor girl any longer – so goodbye. (Thus we are rid of the bugbear.)

MISS L: (sighing with relief)

MRS. DE F: (how noble she is) Do not say it Miss Linton. It is too very obvious (although she considers herself above Miss L. in social standing, Mrs. de F. has to have some outlet at this critical moment) Miss Linton, but I agree with you.

MISS L: (at last untactful) Mrs. de Frills, if it were not the Lord's work, I'd never attend another Mission Meeting!

MRS. DE F: But we must remember that most of these ladies are simply not in our class. They are good, kind, and – shall I say endeavouring? And we owe them our thanks. But they were not born into superior families – and good breeding will out, my dear.

MISS L: Let us leave this nauseating room.

MRS. DE F: You go, Miss Linton, don't think of waiting for *me*. I must stay and collect my things.

MISS L: I hate to leave but I have an appointment with my hairdresser – for tonight's ball, you know. Well, goodbye.

MRS. DE F: Goodbye Miss Linton. (Exit Miss L. daintily, and as becomes her good breeding.)

MRS. DE F: And as for her (gathering her elegant fur) she considers herself in my standing, and talks about those other women as though she were not one of them. Ah well! How little each of us realize what we are! Come, Pom-Pom, we must go – I promised you the leftover patty de fois grass sandwiches, but Mrs. Grunty was here before you. Come along – Pom-Pom. Will you come? Good pup. Come along. (Exeunt Mrs. de F. and dog.)

CURTAIN

Part Four, 1930-1933

(16-19 Years)

December 1930

On Picking

Owed to W.M.W.

(Via William Wordsworth)

Two tooths there are to pick, one nearly done
One not yet started; each a mighty choice,
In both thy nail or finger will rejoice,
They are thy chosen pickings, and such fun!
There came a finger, and with holy glee
It picked and picked, and has not vainly striven,
The foodstuff from its hole at length is driven
One tooth from foodstuff now at length is free:
Of one good pick thy nail hath been bereft,
Then pick, O pick, at that which still is left.
For, high-souled nail, what horror would it be,
Should jaw chew tightly, munching as before
Biting the seed, and eating up the core
Leaving no pick, not one good pick for thee!

A Pewtrid Portrait of Mortal Morbidity: Morbid Maggie

Gaunt, o'er the rank, drab, dirty streets she slinks
With hair made foul by dyes
And with her blood-shot eyes,
She winks.
It is not any wink of gay entice,
But with vile hidden lust
She brings you to the dust
And lice.
In filthy shawl pressed close against her breast
She clutches baby corpse.
Her mind is full of warps –
No rest.
Through dismal night whose skinny cat loud wails
Damned, she is wailing too,
Through lips of slimy blue,
Her ails.
Foul rats! Foul mice! Dead cats!
Dead cats! Dead cats! Dead cats! Dead cats!
And lice.

* When saying such words as 'she winks,' and 'lice,'
please grind or spit out through the teeth.

June 1931

Owed to the Density of a Narrow Woman

A wiry womanless wench is she
   Self-satisfied and smug of face.
Set is her jaw and stern and hard
   Without the essence of a grace.
Her mind is narrow, quick to wrath
   Delights in losing other's pleasure;
She has a military glance
   That counts your downfall as a treasure.
A set, smug, stern, conceited, silly Scotchess
   I hope her face breaks out in ugly blotches

(While watching her settled and puffed up countenance,
and me, the while, seething inwardly.)

August, 1931

The Mosquito's Viewpoint

When you consider a mosquito, do you consider him from an unprejudiced point of view? On this question hangs a difficult matter of justice. If you, reader, were to sum up in detail the character of a mosquito, would you be able to put yourself in his place? Would you be able to detach yourself from your manlike point of view as a prospective meal for a mosquito and consider, judiciously, the virtues and faults of this omnipotent insect? The prejudiced point of view would lead you to say that first, above all things, the mosquito is the cause of an unbearable itch and a red swelling lump; second, that he delights in a mad insolent buzzing at night, demonstrating by your standards, an incomprehensible lack of humour and sense; and third, that he has a generally irritating countenance. That is all, and quite enough, you suppose, sarcastically.

But consider these three features from the mosquito's point of view. You will see that, first, he makes a generous announcement that the war is on – revealing at once his daring and fair nature; second, that he possesses a playful spirit, as illustrated by the lullabies; while third, the aspersion on his countenance is simply an unjust ill-founded accusation. He keeps himself trim and sharp, and never accumulates unwanted probiscus. If, for example, he overeats or overdrinks he realizes that all is vanity and rolls over in some odd, obscure corner, there to die.

But above all the mosquito is agile, and even an all-night buzzing binge does not daunt or exhaust him – he is up early in the morning with his enormous eyes ever on the lookout. And you cannot accuse him of not being keen, or of failing to be a good father; for that matter he is a parent to a thousand and he still feels gay. Besides he helps entomologists to earn their living by being a general nuisance, and thus making it necessary to find ways to eliminate him.

Thoughtful, efficient, worthy, helpful, possessed of a sense of humour, coarse, perhaps, but practical, yet to be appreciated, do you not feel great remorse at having so maligned him? No! Well, neither do we.

Owed to The Countenance of Compton-Ricket

And do you think you are inspiring us?
Words crawl like slugs out of your crooked mouth.

There lies a heavy dullness and a drouth
On ev'ry sentiment you pride yourself to think is firing us.

And fire and drouth are different as the dust
Is different from the flame of flesh and lust.

Lopsidedly you mumble words immortal
With languid, swallowing face you are quite confident that
you will enter

(Probably crowned and strolling through the centre)
Beautiful Poetry's blessed sacred portal.

O man unshaven and of vermin brand!
Too temperate you're more than I can stand!

London, May 28, 1932

This slow night closes in,
Sleepily, sleepily
The buses and the motors starting up
Are faint and muffled sounds in other worlds.
Something is abroad tonight
For this hush is the heart of London,
Like the silence in the room
Of a happy sleeper,
Is more than a common hush.
The stillness is primeval
It is Nature
Walking the ways of her long lost
Ancient haunts.

I can feel her walking through the streets
With her breathless freshness
And every leaf and blossoming tree
Leans out to her.
There is a sudden fragrance
Without a wind, without a sigh
She is passing through,
And even the meanest dandelion
Is a lovelier thing
She floats along
Softly, softly
Like a mother watching her sick child,

Calm
With nothing but a sweet sad love,
Wistful and apprehensive
Watching, watching for a minutest way
To win back her own.
The hours are slipping away
And the old, bad, erring, misguided city sleeps
Like a newborn babe.
Nature so gently, so imperceptibly soft
Walks like the night to view her ancient haunts.

Ottawa *Citizen*
June 21st, 1932
(much regretted and despaired)

No one will ever love me.
Nobody could.
Real love must know
With heart and mind.
He must be void of self,
Exhaulting.
Attraction – yes.
There will be some small fool infatuations,
Both of us hiding behind
A cloak of vanity;
Hiding puffed up – 'What will he think of me?
Will my wit and whims bewitch him
Till he falls?'
O! That I had a noble generous soul
Full, capable of love!

January 3, 1933

You are a brilliant maple tree standing on the edge of a lake. And you are dressed in glory. And you shine like a breathless magnificence. But there below you, your Beauty sobs in the water. And those that have life in them sob too when they see your greatness. The tears run into my eyes when I see you there. For in me you create a longing – a yearning that cannot be put out. I see you strong and gorgeous by the lake – and I crawl home weeping.

This is the end of the Juvenilia: Let us turn from the ways of our Childhood.

1918: Brackley Beach, Prince Edward Island. From left Elizabeth Smart, Helen Smart, friend, and Jane Smart.

1921: 1st row, 2nd from right is Elizabeth Smart; 4th from right is Jane Smart; 3rd row, 1st person from right is Helen Smart.

1922 or 23: Elizabeth and Jane Smart with friends.

1930: Graduation procession of Hatfield Hall School for Girls, Cobourg, Ontario.

Elizabeth Smart, 1932 or 1933.

Letters 1931-1933

Monday sometime
in Nov. I think, 1931
Queen Anne Mansions,
St. James's Park,
London, s.w.1.

Dearest Mummy,

I went lunching with the Crippseses[1] today, having accordingly done my nails twice, cleaned my ears twice, mended two holes in my stockings, twice seen that my dress was spotless, brushed my hair – *speshlee dubl* on open side – and thus departed being, the perfect picture of sweetness, and simplicity, decorum, and what the young girl otta B.*

I arrived – I met Diana – dressed simply and wearing simple low-heeled brown strap shoes – she greeted me simply and with simpleness showing her simple and genteel upbringing – O she was nice too – O yes, verily.

I met dear Lady Cripps, who expressed her utter disappointment that yourn and hern meeting were not to be then – she had a woolly hat – rather spreading and reddish wiry hair like wool striking out on each side. She had simple strapless shoes too with even lower heels, and she was a casual lady – but affable.

We ate – we talked – she asked me to a dance on December 21st. We took a bus – to the Theatre – we sat behind a female Hippopotamus with a hanging garden of Babylon on her head – which she removed at our incessant haranging. We were going to part – each on our separate bus – but I said I was a stranger here myself and was obliged to go by taxi – would they come – which they did under protestation – dear mother darling! They

85

lived miles and miles away and the money meter crept up. O well.

This morning was a realization of our idea of Heaven when I came over from the Bowker's there were 9 letters for *me* and 3 for you, O Heaven! Yea! Veritable Paradise.

I am well and feeling Voluptuous – yea – though – I behave always with Decency and Decorum as befits thy dotter – O most worthy Parent. Remember when thou lookest upon my faults and deficiencies – O my mother – remember when thou cast a disapproving eye, remember – I, thy dotter, loves thee.

(signed) B. Smart

* Misfortune! I forgot my handkerchief! O Horrors! O Depravity!

1 Lady and Sir Stafford Cripps are close friends of the Smart family. Sir Stafford Cripps is the Solicitor General in England.

Dearest Mummy and Daddy,

Yesterday we gave a most successful Sherry-Beer, Honeydew Party – 6-8 oclock – about 70 very handsome, eligible, desirable, and susceptible people being present. I wrote about 70 personal notes to them all! Jane wrote 6-8, Susan about 10 or 12. I quite got into the habit. It was really a great success. There was a lot of noise and jollity and Jane and I worked hard introducing. People who thought they had to go early stayed on – and people who were not strong enough for parties forgot it. And when the party was over who do you think was left as the dregs? Without even an invitation or an innuendo of an eye-inveiglement. Frampton![2] Yes. Actually that stalwart youth. Frampton and Ray Lev and Lady Clodagh Aneon! Lady C.A. and Frampton had a loud discussion (we were all sitting in a sort of circle) about the Law. F. and Ray Lev stayed to dinner (No I didn't even press him) and afterwards we all sat by the fire up in the flat (the party was in the Ping Pong room) and Ray gave us some gorgeous music. Very subtle – don't you think?

I never told you about the meeting in St. James Park about 4 weeks ago – that lasted til 4 o'clock A.M. – did I? No. But you seem to have found out – I wouldn't feel safe at the North Pole. Now I shall give you the gory (or glorious) details. I was bold and bad enough to send F. a Christmas card with nothing but my name and a question mark. (I think myself, that this was quite chaste and as it should be.) He replied with a note which he delivered by hand (but unfortunately I was in Essex) asking me to point out the actual tree – (reached his senses at last). I, when I received the letter, replied in haste (not unmaidenly) that I was free on Sunday. He got Flu and sent me a telegram saying terribly sorry etc. How about next Sun? I waited till the last moment – coyly, of course, and said, in genteel language O.K. – But I said it tersely – and business like – as a true daughter of duty should. Well – he thought perhaps I would be ashamed of his dissipated (?) face if he came to get me here – so he asked me if I would prefer to meet him on the bridge in the beloved park. I replied sweetly O.K.

So we each trembled in our separate spheres and waited for Sunday. It came. It was fresh and full of rain drops.

I put on the red dess with the green spots. It was growing dusk when I got to the bridge. He was there. Looking like an artist in a checked coat and his perennial umbrella. We went, very self-consciously to look at the tree – because he almost admitted that he knew which one it was. And I knew he knew – and he knew I knew he knew etc. etc. Then, after admiring the Pelicans and the emotional curves of the various trees we adjourned to the Criterion for tea – it was sprinkling rain quite prolifickly before we got there – and I dare say there was water all over my nose. We had tea and were both to finish the last meringue (the squirting kind). But we had really sat there until the seat beneath us grew hard in indignation. Then we sauntered out into the street. F. asked me if I had any engagements for the evening. I said 'no never at that hour had he?' – He replied 'No' – & when he had he always broke them.

So that was that.

We walked all around London in the wet darkness & dim

lights – we walked across the Thames on an old black bridge. We even ran up the Strand & the old Law Courts.

Well we walked till I had a blister on my heel – (I didn't mention it. I was stoic to a dregree) then – he took a taxi & we went to the Ivy. (Gee!! Age?) & we ate a terrifically expensive dinner – lobster, crab, turkey, etc. & I drank so much water that I never will drink too much water again before going out for the evening.

Well, after that – we still were not yawning – so F. said let's go for a drive. B. said O.K. again – even though he might erroneously think her a yes-girl. So we both got F.'s car – a rickety open 5-seater – which was garaged up town & then we drove for miles & there was even a brightish moon at times – But B. was not carried away & B. & F. behaved as though E.L.S. was in the back seat. Well, then we thought of the time; it was about 2 o'clock so B. wondered if Susan Somerset would be worried. She wasn't all goose-flesh at the thought, but it crossed her mind that to give other people anxiety isn't a nice, good thing to do. So F. and B. stopped at a pay telephone & rang up the Basil St. Hotel. B. after ringing Susan for several minutes tried Jane's room – This Jane answered at once & said all right – Susan was asleep – she knew I was all right with F. But just before I got on to Jane – F. had to deposit another 6 pence. So we came home.

That's all.

I had lunch with Malcolm MacDonald one day. I went to 10, Downing St., but we didn't eat there because there was a meeting or something which Malcolm said might bore me and would certainly bore him. We looked at his books & then had lunch at St. Ermine's. It was fun telling the taxi man to go to 10, Down-

ing St! Malcolm said that if his father was at Checkers this week-
end, he wanted me to go down. However, his father wasn't & so
no one can go there. However, perhaps I'll go some other time.
Malcolm is darling.

We (Jane and I) had tea at Katharine Goodson's[3] the same
day. Michelle Hanboring was there – I was talking to her for
quite a while – & she played to us. She is a remarkable child – not
only musically, but every way. She & her father are very keen
on collecting Persian & Indian & Chinese antiques.

Mrs. Allward has been so kind to us. We have been there several times. Last Sunday Susan went too.

There was one error in the party though. Evidently, on Mrs.
Allward's invitation I put the hour 4-6 instead of 6-8 & I evidently did the same thing to Mrs. Northern. Anyway the 3 of
them arrived at tea time & there were some awkward pauses.
Jane came in & found them loose in the hall downstairs – she
brought them up & gave them tea & Susan & she tried to enter-
tain them. Later I came in from my music lessons & found them
all sitting sad-eyed in the living room. Mrs. Northern was making positive, loud platitudinal remarks with no depth or meaning
in them. She was certainly not making a contact with Mrs. Allward. O well! it all came to an end – & we went down stairs & the
party began. Harris Brown clutched me by the arm as he scru-
tinized the room fervently asking me if there was anyone there
he wanted to meet!

We were all thrilled about Michael Swabey.[4] I let everyone
know. Frampton exclaimed when I told him, 'Fancy your
mother a grandmother! She doesn't look ½ old as I feel!' Everyone is laughing at the idea of you being at the top of 3 genera-

tions! Everyone is always saying how charming you are & what lovely manners you have & how clever you are. Mrs. Watt[5] almost speaks of you with a break in her voice. She is missing you terribly. She is not a bit well & is looking very white & has got that pale wrinkled creased look of old ladies. She is also very nervous. She has been sweet to us. Jane has been skating with Sholto.[6] Sholto looks terrible. He must be anemic. He is an ashen gray colour & looks harassed. We were amazed how shy he was at the party. He is still an enigma!

Katharine Goodson has been *marvellous* to me – you must thank her some way – I can't.

I am studying English – but am not taking the Oxford Exam this Spring because I would have had to give up my music completely till then. I am doing 4 hours of solid technique a day – 2 of them on K.G.'s dumb piano!! As well as another hour of Theory and Harmony.

Tonight I am going out with Ben Thomas – He had a very serious burst appendix. He is vurra nice and cute.

The London streets are full of pastel tulips & fragrant mimosa. It is mild today, & I walked alone out to Regent's Park, & Primrose Hill in the sun, after my English lesson. I never do anything but my 4 hours of Technique in the morning – & I let NOTHING interfere with it. Not even F.!

Susan still likes us. She is good at mending our clothes & washing our stockings.

The Clifford Curzon's baby was still-born ––

with love from
Betty

1 The Basil Street Hotel, London, s.w.1, is the hotel where Elizabeth and her sister Jane are living with their chaperone Susan Somerset.
2 Meredith Frampton, (r.a.) is a painter Elizabeth had met in London.
3 Katharine Goodson is a concert pianist under whom she is studying the piano.
4 Michael Swabey is the new son of Helen (Smart) and Alan Swabey.
5 Mrs. (Alfred) Watt, m.b.e. is a close friend of the Smart family, and one of the first women in Canada to receive an m.a. She organized the Country Women's Institute in England.
6 Sholto is the son of Mrs. Watt.

B.S.H.
Knightsbridge
Feb. 16, 1933

Dearest Daddy,

I got your letter today and I am still all shaking with meaness. It seems almost impossible to get anything done nowadays – whenever I do get a minute I have to write an essay for English or read *Lives* or *Works*. *Three* seems to be a turbulant number – sort of confusing. Just lately I have been feeling rather stale & depressed – & it seems such an ungrateful thing to feel now. What I think it is really is never having any time for thinking or being alone at all – for the reading and the contemplation you say you miss. Before I have always been alone a great part of the time – last year Mummy and I each went our own ways – in little moments – & then I had time to sort of get adjusted & laugh at the right things. If you just lie on the sofa & contemplate the chimney pots for an hour, you feel beautifully richer and fuller – everything working easily – but if you don't you seem to be walking in a mist listlessly without any direction. And of course – for me it always takes longer to draw the power out of Chimney Pots than out of trees and hills.

I wish, since I got your letter that I had taken my Exam. No, I don't – My music would have gone completely. It was Miss Mayne (my new music teacher) and Katharine Goodson who tilted the scales in this direction. To give up my music would seem to be cheating her – as if I had been pretending all the time & deceiving when she said she didn't take "Butterflies." She is still doing so much for me – giving me odd lessons – & her dumb piano – & all kinds of mottos of her own self – like the one she put on a picture she gave me:

> I can't does nothing
> I'll try does wonders!
> I will does everything!!

Also I heard Clifford Curzon play & spoke to him afterwards – I wish he had been able to take me. He is so inspiring & he shows you daylight. Music is a different thing from what it used to be. Then it was something secret & sacred of my own. Now it is an intricate profession – more intellectual than emotional – because of course, all that brain and muscle work has to come first & there is a tremendous joy in feeling your fingers straining to be off like horses before the beginning of a race. But it means something different.

I wrote to John Cripps about Oxford – & he answered me – rather thinking I wouldn't like it much – mostly on the grounds of restrictions & climate. He when he wrote had no idea what I wanted to do there so of course his letter was rather general – but I am going to send him some details and discuss the matter thoroughly. I like him & he really has a keen mind. We had dinner & games at the Stafford Cripps last Wednesday. It was so nice and like our own home that Jane & I were quite homesick. Diana & her mother & the 'Per(?)' Weaver adopted son – a brother and sister (*very* nice and sort of quietly intelligent – you know) and another boy rather like Jack Macdonnell only not so juvenilely objectionable. It was marvellous to have intelligent – non-stodgy and not platitudiness conversation – free & easy but stimulating. Afterwards we played games like Check the Chinamen (multiple Canfield) & other unstreperous things. Then Sir Stafford came in – he really is rather like you sometimes and he is so young. Very cute and boyish. Lady Cripps was darling, rather passive and placid but motherly abstractly, & she kissed me goodby. Yes going home in the taxi we actually felt acutely homesick.

My English teacher, a Mrs. Paynter is a stimulating lady – though outwardly of the austere forbidding unfeminine type. She is fairly fleshy & has straight scant bobbed hair & round head. I was terrified at first – but fortunately the first time she fired questions at me they were ones I knew & she isn't paralliz-ing. When we were going along reading Spenser for instance, & a mention is made of Elizabeth's victories – or something – she suddenly says – with a pistol at my head – what was the date of the Spanish Armada? & she doesn't whine it like some of them do. It is fun.

I still have a weakness for morbid poetry but not poor morbid poetry. Spenser is the latest poet I have 'discovered.' I have a passion for him. He is luxurious and voluptuous and rich. You have that feeling – how shall I describe it – like when you look at something rich and gorgeous to eat and say 'Fhyoop-Ka!' Do you know?

I adore this stanza from *The Fairy Queen* – Why was I never introduced to Spenser before? I never had read a line until this year. Isn't this succulent?

> And by his side rode loathsome Gluttony
> Deformed creature, on a filthie swine,
> His belly was upbloune with luxury,
> And eke with fatnesse swollen were his eyne

And like a crane his neck was long and fine,
With which he swallowed up excessive feast,
For want whereof poor people oft did pine;
And all the way, most like a brutish beast,
He spued up his gorge, that all did him deteast.

Talking of bellies being up blown with luxury, I saw Ethel Jane a couple of days ago. She is still fierce and vampish & though I do hate her, it is rather fascinating to watch something so inhuman & hysterical. She works all the time at her bridge club & it seems to be doing quite well. 'Bell' has developed into – Oh! even more than a sister – she is arrogant & puts me in my place. Quite rightly too! But if Ethel Jane looks at any thing or any person I love – I sort of feel as if she had destroyed it. All exposed and humiliated.

Mrs. Kirkhoffer was cremated on Tuesday and we went to the Funeral Service in the little Queen Anne's Upturned Footstool Church in Smith Square. It didn't seem right. She was so earthly and gay. Death is an awful shock – it stays in your mind for ages afterwards. K.K.B. and Mary were at the Church & followed the coffin out. K.K.B. looked drowned in tears – her face was all full of tremendous sadness – nothing but sorrow. She looked as if she had given up all struggles & just abandoned herself to tears. I think she was in Bristol at the time – but she may have got back.

I think the last time Mrs. Kirkhoffer went out it was with me. I took her to see the film – *The Blue Light* (a marvellous German legend in the Dolomite Alps – with the poetry unspoiled & hardly any dialogue – I saw it more than once!) & all the way going and coming & at teatime – she talked about whether she would be cremated or whether she wouldn't – & what she had told Gordon to do with her ashes. She played every part – sort of revelled in each – right up to the very end. But it was rather pathetic when she took my hand & asked me if I loved her – an afraidness for her & when Jane went to see her she would reassure herself by telling Jane that I loved her – I had *said* so. Of course – she couldn't afford clothes or theatres or anything – she did that last year too – but this year with a little more truth and sadness.

Death doesn't – can't mean much – until you actually see the coffin – then it's a shock. I think animals have a better way of dying – they do it quietly & secretly & modestly. They just go away & die – & are never seen or heard of again – except of course when they are actually killed. It is a so much better taste – nothing ghastly or morbid. You are saddened a little because you don't see them anymore – but that is all. How do they do it?

I am reading Thomas Hardy now. I have finished *Tess of the D'Urbervilles* and I am nearly through *Far From the Madding Crowd.* I was a little disappointed at first in the almost affected style – that must have been a fault of the age or something – but I soon forgot that. It gets more inevitable & heavier & heavier. I don't really think that Mary Webb and Hardy are very much alike – I had often heard them likened to each other. Mary Webb's Nature is more intimate & rapturous & her happy endings are more upsetting than her tragic ones. Hardy is Man, man, himself, not Nature – only as a background. O well – I love them both. But I am going to live in mountains when I know more than I know now.

On Saturday I am going out with Meredith Frampton – that will be a 'golden moment.' He is so comforting and stimulating – why? Because he has ideas of his own – not educational ideas &

he is a real artist all the way through. What is the best thing in anyone, I think almost, is silence. He is marvellous to be silent with – just sit & say nothing – you think a lot & you feel verra happy. Isn't that a rare gift? to be stimulating to another's mind without saying anything? Well, that's what he does to me & I feel bursting with content & exciting peace. O well – I will keep my head. I think he understands the country, too. He listens to the trees laughing in the wind in the right way. But of course I may be a foolish female carried away by imagination. *You* stimulate thought without saying anything. It was *you* who taught me to appreciate these things. *Selah.*

Well – it is very way past my practising hour and if I write anymore you will have to take a day off from the office to read it.

Goodbye – Love Oh Love

Betty

P.S. I had a very cute verse from Sir Robert Greig. He accepted for the party but got flu and couldn't come. The Barrington-Wards were here – they are darlings – what the A.A. Milne's *should* be like, but aren't.

Sunday, June 18,
1933
Göteborg, Germany

Dear Mummy,

I actually am going to Sweden. I believe I have just split an infinitive, but who cares anyway?

The last three weeks have been rather gay. But the nice kind of gay. Bread and cheese and high thinking. *You* know. Nice. I was up at Oxford for a few days with Graham.[1] Oh! It was all very respectable and quite quite conventional. We lunched or dined everyday with a magnificent quite young don of philosophy who had a bald spot and looked not unlike Frampton. Einstein was up there and he was translating his speech for him. Oh! a great man. Very stimulating. We ran into Oliver Gatty and he asked us to supper. We motored out to Abingdon with him and then returned to another don's room where there was a whole stag party of dons ranging from 26 to 66, at least there was about 8 or 10 of them – and dons are every expansive. Oliver was very nice and actually *jumped 3 times* for joy when he recognized Graham. The weather was heavenly – as hot as Kingsmere at its best. One day Gilbert[2] motored us to the Stafford Cripps for tea. (Lady Cripps had sent me a note asking me to come by way of Graham when he was down before.) Sir Stafford was there and went off somewhere to a speech. Diana was sick again. She seems very delicate. While we were watching the tennis some Morris dancers came along. Real yokels dressed in ribbons & bells – with an ancient crooked fiddler who fiddled all out of tune & said he had taught some airs to Percy Grainger. We were given some ancient cake and beguiled with their hoppety dances which they did with perfectly vacant, open-mouthed faces. Some of them were quite older men – one a stubby little fellow of 57 or so with a mustache. They all had on hobb-clobby boots & took pride in their art. Lady Cripps was sweet to me & wants me to go down & visit them if I can when I get back. John was still at Oxford. Several other people were there.

Another day Gilbert (the Philosopher) motored us to the downs in Berkshire & we all wandered around. You would love Gilbert Ryle. He is big.

I had coctails with Harry Hodson and his wife. They have quite a big causal house with a big iron gate – tucked in a corner in Fulham with its back to the houses on the main road. It has a tiny green & flag-stone garden with a tree planted by Nell Gwyn in it. The house itself is beautifully old and informal. There are two rooms – one three steps lower than the other – like a studio with big sky-light windows & down to the garden there is a nice sprawly divan and comfortable chairs. Heeps of books in shelves all along the walls (which arn't their's) and a piano and papers. Margaret Hodson, the fortunate girl (!) is very nice indeed. She is slim & has very fair blonde hair which she wears in a roll of curls – almost like mine only a roll and not behind her ears. She is not pretty but attractive – pregnant perhaps. Definitely physical with a large mouth – lipsticked. She is fun – *not* an intellectual at all, but bright & has a real sense of humour. She is natural too. More simple, on the whole, than I would have expected from Harry. She dresses nicely & puts them on well – and teases him & tells him not to roll the rug down. He adores her & looks at her with blinking eyes and pride. Harry's sister also came in. Dressed in the English way that Helen despises – with a largish stiff ungracious hat and waistless clothes – but she seemed nice and friendly too. The little wife, though is rather loveable. She has a little thin white face and quite sharp nose. She adores London and England – never having been there before and is quite naive about everything. Twenty years old and gay in spirit. I commend Harry.

Kenneth Lindsay took us out one night (remember? the man you found on the information that his name was Walter – friend of Brooke Claxton's?) & we got Mary Bowker at the last minute because we missed connections with Georgie Claudet. Mary was not a success. If she would only be natural or stop being jealous of other people, or stop trying to be important by making inane criticisms. But she enjoyed being asked & we did her well with white ties, my white dress and Monseignier. Besides 2 very eligible gents.

Tom Davies & John Williams continue to take me out till the bitter end. In fact, John saw me off at the station yesterday & Tom wanted to but his mother was rather sick. I had them both thoroughly chastened & they always called for me without protest.

I lunched with Katharine Goodson yesterday & Graham called for me afterwards – I told her he was going to so she kept the strawberries, coffee and liquer waiting for him. Graham will tell you all the gory details – anyway, I expect you will worm them out of him. He came down to the brat and Robin, Doreen and Sholto also did. They were in another part of the train with Mrs. Watt. Graham and Sholto laughed at each others' jokes.[3]

I lunched with Mrs. Allward on Friday. Don has been quite seriously ill. His heart. He is better now but has to be very careful. They are sending him to the sea. She gave me a book.

I was very sorry to hear about Mr. Lett. I am writing to Katie. Also Chelsea Willis.

Thank you for your letter & for the pound. It was very handy for tipping Bell. It was a very successful stay there. Ethel Jane confessed that she had thought I wasn't going to like it. She is incapable of a lot of things, but she lavished material kindnesses on me & mended my things & went shopping with me once. Really, I was very happy there. One night, though, it was rather amusing. Little John Williams – a very gentle, sweet, considerate little boy, was saying goodbye to me on the steps. He was trying, I could see, to get up his courage to say something really nice when a voice from above bellowed in a loud whisper, 'Graham!! is that you Graham?' I whispered loudly back, 'No! No! It's not Graham.' She said again, 'Graham! is that you? Well, BEAT IT.' Poor little John shook my hand with terror & fled like a frightened rabbit.

The boat is lovely & clean with heaps of people on board. Swedes. I think I shall love Sweden and things Swedish. Mrs. Watt is very happy.

Goodbye. Love to all.

Betty

P.S. I am thrilled about Alan and Helen. Do send me a picture of Baby.

1 Graham Sprye, a Canadian journalist, diplomat, advocate of public broadcasting and political organizer, is a friend of the family and mentor of Elizabeth's.

2 Gilbert Ryle is an Oxford Philosopher and author of *A Concept of Mind.*

3 Elizabeth is accompanying Mrs. Watt to Sweden and Germany where she will attend conferences of the Country Women's Organizations. Robin is Mrs. Watt's other son and Doreen his wife.

July 27, 1933,
c / o Herr W. Fick,
Haus Christa,
Braunlage Oberharz,
Germany.

Dear Daddy,

I am going back to Canada. I am still at Bad-Nauheim *now*, August, & I want to stay there, please. It's the place for me. Jane goes to McGill and I can stay at home. Anyway, whatever happens, I am going back to Canada, & I should like to stay there. Jane must go to McGill – that seems to me natural & inevitable & the only right thing. Well, I suppose that's settled now. Really! I simply *can't* imagine or concoct the future – I simply *can't* think farther than today. (No *don't* tell me there's no such word.) But I do know that I want to be in Canada. I should be content to be 'the comfort in the home' & pass ash-trays gracefully, as long as I can work, & I don't suppose anyone will stop me from doing that!

It's a hot sultry day, very hot for Germany. In a few minutes I go to a bath in a huge brown wooden tub. I am reading James Joyce, Virginia Woolf, D.H. Lawrence, and Richard Jeffries. I love being in Europe for the pretty, cheap editions you can get. I like to love the outside of a book as well as the in – but if I don't like what's in it I even hate to touch it & make it mine. I am sure that's a very moral sign! Anyway for 35 cents a week I can get all the literature I want & more. As Barrie said, & as Graham advises, & as you know & as I know, the only way to write is to write – discipline and will uniting. Well, I'm mustering all I will. I owe a lot to Graham, you know – he gives the right advice. It is rather early in the morning & I read terribly late last night when the lights are meant to go out at ten – that is probably why this letter is so incoherent & dumb. By the way, did you know the German word for 'stupid' is 'dumm'?

I had a lovely excursion with a German gentleman of 70 on Wednesday. We started out at 7:20 in the morning, took a train for seventeen miles & then walked 30 kilometres – through hilly woods & by huge blonde fields of wheat where peasants worked with scarves over their hair & royal blue dresses on. We had buttermilk in several little red-coned sunny villages that smell like barnyards & in the cobbles – the one narrow windy road – the hens walk about. The people are like the peasants in *The Blue Light* – the old ones bent, with brown and wrinkled faces. And they are all so friendly and real – even if they do stick their fingers in the buttermilk to see if it's sour. The only thing was that Herr Wirtz didn't speak English & if he wanted to say anything, no matter if we were toiling up a hill in the sun with hardly enough breath to think, he would invariably stop, clutch me by the arm or tap me, & say in too vigouress and extant tones, what he had to say, & if I didn't understand he went on to explain. He could never speak without stopping & it's so much easier to walk than stand. But he is a darling Herr really & it was a lovely day – and I don't know how many miles 30 kilometres is – but the last 4 kilometres – which were along a real road across the plain were the longest I've ever trod!

Mrs. Watt is calling now. I must go. See you in August. I'm sorry this letter is so Dumm.

With love from

Betty

Dearest Mummy,

I shall probably be home not long after this & I shall be home to stay. There is no use going to other countries before you are all settled – like dough; you get lost and – no it's no good. You must stay in your own country unless you want to be a loose vague dangling end. It's all right; it's good to go later when you are *done,* for a sort of research and investigation, but Oh! I wish I could make you see how vital it is to have the strength of your own country behind you. So I do hope Jane is going to McGill – Oh! I do hope so. I feel *urgent* about it. I want to be in Canada – I don't care where or how, excepting that I don't specially want to have Hazel Hope Bowles for a chaperone. Anyway I want to be at home in Canada, & get a hold of things.

London is too fascinating; it gets you. It seems to me that it's like a drowning person that clutches onto whatever comes near it. Well, I was in its clutches & now I am free & I am swimming to shore, & when I get there I want to climb mountains.

Does that sound silly? Yes. I suppose so. But I mean it. And I wish you could see it too.

On Monday (this is Saturday night) Mrs. Watt and I are leaving for London. Mrs. Allward has asked us to stay with them so that will be lovely. I shall get a brat ten days later & be soon in Canada. Frampton, unfortunately, says he can not go. He had a bad crash in his car & a lady who was his passenger had her face badly cut by glass. There are legal proceedings & things, because they want to convict the other driver. I still shall try to persuade him, though I do feel it's a hopeless task. Mrs. Allward has been darling, sending me postcards & notes, & such a sweet invitation. I am verra excited about going back.

I am trying to get back before Kingsmere gets too cold.

Mummy, I do pray that you see what I mean about Jane & I staying in Canada. The other is a sort of disintegration – I don't think that's quite the right word, but it means a falling apart. It's one truth that has come slowly & surely home to me – from living & from reading & from listening, & at the moment, it's the one thing I'm really sure of. If I stayed over here any longer, I should lose hold. And Jane – oh she would be lost too. It was good what we had. That much was good, & we shall always be terribly glad we had it – but an inch more we would be over the edge. It would be too much. Oh! Beware the Ides of March! A stitch in time saves 9. It's the last straw that breaks the camel's back. Oh! Do you understand?

I am very pally in German now and I *verstehe* everything almost that's vital anyway. I have climbed Wurmburg, the Brohen and Achtermann twice, once before breakfast in the early sun after I had slept out all night.

Mrs. Watt is very well.

Jane goes to McGill. I am the Joy in the home.

Goodbye & love to you.

Heaps of love,
Betty

Braunlage
Germany
Aug. 12th /33

Dearest Mummy,

I shall probably be home not long after this and I shall be home to stay. There is no use going to other countries before you are all settled — like dough; you get lost & — no its no good. You must stay in your own country unless you want to be a loose vague dumpling end. Its all right, its good to go later when you are done, for a sort of research, investigation, but Oh! I wish I could make you see how vital it is to have the strength of your own country behind you. So I do hope Jane is going to McGill — Oh! I do hope so. I feel Urgent about it.

I want to be in Canada —

3

I don't care when or how,
— except ing that I don't
specially want to have
Hazel Hope Bowles for a
chaperone. Anyway I want to be
at present in Canada and
get hold of things.

London is too fascinating;
it gets you. It seems to me
that it's like a drowning
person that clutches onto
whatever comes near it.
Well, I was in its clutches,
now I am free & I am
swimming for shore, + when I
get there I want to climb
mountains.

Does that sound silly? Yes,
I suppose so. But I mean it.
And I wish you would see
it too.

On Monday, (This is Saturday

Design: Gordon Robertson
Typesetting in Aldus: Nelson Adams
Printed in Canada

For a list of other books
write for our catalogue
or call us at (416) 979-2217

THE COACH HOUSE PRESS
401 (rear) Huron Street
Toronto, Canada M5S 2G5